The HEAL Program®

Learner Workbook

Advanced - Level 3

HEAL Acknowledgments

We would like to acknowledge and thank the following individuals and organizations for their support in the development of this publication.

Literacy for Life

Executive Director and HEAL Concept
Joan Buckman Peterson

Development Team
Fiona Van Gheem, Sara Nye,
Sabrina Kurtz-Rossi, Julie McKinney

Graphic Design
Lara Eckerman

Expert Reviewer
Mary Kay Dineen, MD

Invaluable Others
Sarah Peterson, MD, Natalie Miller Moore,
Anne E. Mitchell, Katharine Watson Block,
Williamsburg Health Foundation

Literacy for Life HEAL Instructors and Learners

Credits

Stock Photography, Illustrations and Graphics by

©iStockphoto; ©Shutterstock; United States Department of Agriculture; National Heart, Lung, and Blood Institute; National Institutes of Health; US Department of Health & Human Services; United States Pharmacopeial Convention; Food and Drug Administration

Elena Elisseeva; pioneer111; Givaga; PeJo29; Jacek Chabraszewski; Thomas Perkins; Pathathai Chungyam; PhotoGoricki; Zerbor; deeepblue; Nicole Hofmann; sihuo0860371; Aneese; epantha; raw206; saintho; frender; anatols; m-gucci; jean-marie guyon; SIphotography; takoburito; Simone van den Berg; KatarzynaBialasiewicz; Catalin205; gbh007; danielle71; vadimguzhva; Tonpicknick; Kay_motec; kosziv; Christopher Futcher; Eraxion; Sunshine_Art; subjug; fcafotodigital; Carlos Gawronski; dcdr; Diane Labombarbe; hoozone; SelectStock; Michael Kurtz; Gregory_DUBUS; gilaxia; Preben Gramstrup; Juanmonino; laflor; simonmcconico; Asia_Images; baona; Visiofutura; Ocskaymark; kupicoo; gradyreese; Christopher Futcher; Kemter; Dominik Pabis; BraunS; Alexandru Kacso; Steve Debenport; alvarez; abadonian; Roel Smart; Vichly44; kazoka30; Tatomm; Charles Mann; kosmozoo; AndreyPopov; Catalin205; erikreis; asikkk; Yuri_Arcurs; M_a_y_a; SelectStock; dina2001; kazoka30; Tarzhanova; fcafotodigital; Gary Alvis; gbh007; m-imagephotography; mactrunk; stevecoleimages; manifeesto; monkeybusinessimages; peterspiro; rogerashford; Daviles; andresr; Creativeye99; MagMos; nensuria; MichaelJay; lzf; worac; Cathy Yeulet; anna1311; loops7; anna1311; Maksym Narodenko; phittavas; Volosina; hawk111; anna1311; Lauri Patterson; DonNichols; AndreaAstes; whitewish; ClaudioVentrella; Floortje; Coprid; cynoclub; LeventKonuk; obewon; anna1311; Kaan Ates; John Solie; Arsty; Greg Nicholas; Todor Tsvetkov; FangXiaNuo; Valentyna Chukhlyebova/©Shutterstock; Edyta Pawlowska/©Shutterstock; Melinda Fawver/©Shutterstock; David Smart/©Shutterstock

This resource is designed for educational purposes only and is not a substitute for informed medical advice. You should not use this information to diagnose or treat a health problem or disease without consulting a doctor or qualified health care provider. This book includes references to other resources and links to websites to help you find health information and services. Literacy for Life does not necessarily endorse or recommend the organizations that produce these resources, websites, or the information that they provide.

Table of Contents

Lesson 4: Appointments

Vocabulary
Preparing for a Doctor's Appointment
Making a Doctor's Appointment
Screening Tests
On My Own: My Health History Form

Lesson 5: Talking to the Doctor

Vocabulary
Being Prepared for a Doctor's Visit
Describing Your Symptoms
Answering Questions
Talking to the Doctor
What to Do If You Don't Understand
On My Own: My Symptoms and Questions

Lesson 6: It's My Health

Vocabulary
Taking Care of My Teeth
Body Mass Index (BMI) Chart
Impacts of Smoking, Alcohol and Drugs on the Body
Taking Care of Stress
My Rights and Responsibilities
My Health Journal
Own My Own: Finding Health Information Online

Lesson 7: Review

How to Keep Using This Workbook

Where To Go For Healthcare

You are the **most important person** responsible for your health.

Free or low cost clinics in my area:

_____

_____

_____

Urgent care clinics in my area:

_____

_____

_____

At the doctor's office, ask:

1. What is my main problem?
2. What do I need to do?
3. Why is it important for me?

What to do in an emergency:

If it is life-threatening, call **911** If it is not life-threatening, call your doctor or go to Urgent Care.

Hospitals and health centers have interpreters and interpreter phones in many languages

If you need an interpreter, you just need to ask! Say, "I need an interpreter, please."

My Healthcare Providers

Fill out the following information for your Primary Doctor and Specialist Doctors.

Primary Doctor:

My Primary Care Doctor's Name: _____

Doctor's Phone Number: _____

My Health Insurance Plan: _____

My Health Insurance Number: _____

* For more insurance information, visit healthcare.gov

Other Specialist Doctors:

Other Specialist Doctor's Name: _____

Specialty: _____ Phone Number: _____

Other Specialist Doctor's Name: _____

Specialty: _____ Phone Number: _____

My Urgent Care Center: _____

Phone Number: _____

1

Lesson 1: Healthy Eating

One big part of being healthy is eating in a healthy way. This means eating the right kinds of food, and the right amounts. Eating too much food can cause you to get too heavy (fat). This is called being **overweight**. Being overweight can cause poor health and sickness like heart disease and diabetes. Eating food from each of the **Food Groups** will give your body the nutrients it needs to stay healthy.

The 5 Food Groups:
- Fruits
- Vegetables
- Grains
- Protein
- Dairy

One way to help you eat healthy is to use the MyPlate picture. This picture shows that half your plate should be filled with fruits and vegetables at every meal. To eat the right amount, try to fit your foods on one plate the way the picture shows.

What will I learn?

- Eat healthy to be healthy
- Eat more fruits and vegetables
- A healthy plate includes foods from all food groups
- Eating too much and being overweight can cause health problems

Vocabulary

What new words do you want to learn? Write the words and their definitions here.

Words	Definitions

Nutrients in Food

Match the number of each word below with the correct description below. The first one is done for you.

1. Carbohydrates
2. Proteins
3. Fats
4. Fiber
5. Vitamins
6. Calcium
7. Iron
8. Sodium

Number	Description
7	Helps the blood do its job
	Build muscles and repairs cells
	Is another word for salt
	Give you energy
	Store energy for later use
	Help fight sickness
	Keeps bones strong
	Helps get rid of waste

What's On Your Plate?

Focus on the four photos in the area outlined in yellow below.

What's on your plate?

ChooseMyPlate.gov

Fruits | Grains | Dairy | Vegetables | Protein

Before you eat, think about what and how much food goes on your plate or in your cup or bowl. Over the day, include foods from all food groups: vegetables, fruits, whole grains, low-fat dairy products, and lean protein foods.

Make half your plate fruits and vegetables.

Make at least half your grains whole.

Switch to skim or 1% milk.

Vary your protein food choices.

What's On Your Plate?

Focus on the text in the area outlined in yellow below.

Vegetables	Fruits	Grains	Dairy	Protein Foods
Eat more red, orange, and dark-green veggies like tomatoes, sweet potatoes, and broccoli in main dishes. Add beans or peas to salads (kidney or chickpeas), soups (split peas or lentils), and side dishes (pinto or baked beans), or serve as a main dish. Fresh, frozen, and canned vegetables all count. Choose "reduced sodium" or "no-salt-added" canned veggies.	Use fruits as snacks, salads, and desserts. At breakfast, top your cereal with bananas or strawberries; add blueberries to pancakes. Buy fruits that are dried, frozen, and canned (in water or 100% juice), as well as fresh fruits. Select 100% fruit juice when choosing juices.	Substitute whole-grain choices for refined-grain breads, bagels, rolls, breakfast cereals, crackers, rice, and pasta. Check the ingredients list on product labels for the words "whole" or "whole grain" before the grain ingredient name. Choose products that name a whole grain first on the ingredients list.	Choose skim (fat-free) or 1% (low-fat) milk. They have the same amount of calcium and other essential nutrients as whole milk, but less fat and calories. Top fruit salads and baked potatoes with low-fat yogurt. If you are lactose intolerant, try lactose-free milk or fortified soymilk (soy beverage).	Eat a variety of foods from the protein food group each week, such as seafood, beans and peas, and nuts as well as lean meats, poultry, and eggs. Twice a week, make seafood the protein on your plate. Choose lean meats and ground beef that are at least 90% lean. Trim or drain fat from meat and remove skin from poultry to cut fat and calories.

For a 2,000-calorie daily food plan, you need the amounts below from each food group.
To find amounts personalized for you, go to ChooseMyPlate.gov.

Eat 2½ cups every day	Eat 2 cups every day	Eat 6 ounces every day	Get 3 cups every day	Eat 5½ ounces every day
What counts as a cup? 1 cup of raw or cooked vegetables or vegetable juice; 2 cups of leafy salad greens	**What counts as a cup?** 1 cup of raw or cooked fruit or 100% fruit juice; ½ cup dried fruit	**What counts as an ounce?** 1 slice of bread; ½ cup of cooked rice, cereal, or pasta; 1 ounce of ready-to-eat cereal	**What counts as a cup?** 1 cup of milk, yogurt, or fortified soymilk; 1½ ounces natural or 2 ounces processed cheese	**What counts as an ounce?** 1 ounce of lean meat, poultry, or fish; 1 egg; 1 Tbsp peanut butter; ½ ounce nuts or seeds; ¼ cup beans or peas

USDA U.S. Department of Agriculture • Center for Nutrition Policy and Promotion
August 2011
CNPP-25
USDA is an equal opportunity provider and employer

Cut back on sodium and empty calories from solid fats and added sugars

Look out for salt (sodium) in foods you buy. Compare sodium in foods and choose those with a lower number.

Drink water instead of sugary drinks. Eat sugary desserts less often.

Make foods that are high in solid fats—such as cakes, cookies, ice cream, pizza, cheese, sausages, and hot dogs—occasional choices, not every day foods.

Limit empty calories to less than 260 per day, based on a 2,000 calorie diet.

Be physically active your way

Pick activities you like and do each for at least 10 minutes at a time. Every bit adds up, and health benefits increase as you spend more time being active.

Children and adolescents: get 60 minutes or more a day.

Adults: get 2 hours and 30 minutes or more a week of activity that requires moderate effort, such as brisk walking.

Healthy Meal Planning

Create a healthy meal plan for breakfast, lunch and dinner. Write the foods on the plate.

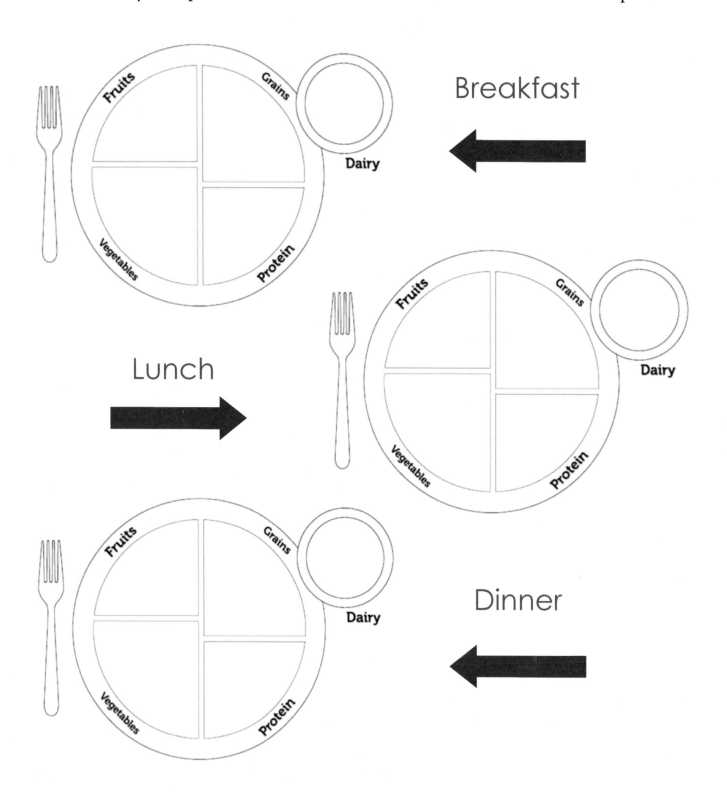

Compare Cereals

Find the information on the label and compare the two cereal boxes.

	Cereal 1	Cereal 2
Serving Size		
% DV Total Fat		
% DV Sodium		
% DV Dietary Fiber		
Sugars (g)		
Iron		
What do you notice about the list of ingredients?		

Different Kinds of Fats

Check √ the foods that contain good fats. Write a healthier option for the foods that contain bad fats.

How to tell the difference?

Most fats that come from animals are bad, but lean protein like fish and chicken are very healthy and don't have a lot of bad fat.

Good fats help you to manage your moods, stay on top of your mental game, fight fatigue and even control your weight.

Food	Good or Bad?
Olives	√
Cream	Low-fat milk
Ice Cream	
Avocados	
Salmon	
Butter	
Red Meat	
Potato Chips	
Cheeseburger	
Peanut Butter	
Walnuts	

On My Own: Substituting Ingredients

Look at the recipe below for tacos, and see how this dinner can become healthier with just a few changes!

Taco Dinner

Regular Ingredients	Healthy Substitutions
Ground beef	Ground turkey or chicken
Hard shells or soft white tortillas	Whole wheat tortillas
Taco seasoning packet	Low-sodium seasoning packet
Sour cream	Use less or use low-fat sour cream
Cheese	Use less or use low-fat cheese
Lettuce, tomato, avocado	Use lots of these

In the chart below, use what you have learned today to make a recipe from home a little bit healthier.

Recipe For _____

Regular Ingredients	Healthy Substitutions

Lesson 2: Medicine

Do you know the different between a prescription medicine and over-the-counter medicine? What do you need know about medicine?

Anyone can buy an over-the-counter medicine but only someone with a prescription from their doctor can buy a prescription medicine.

Medicine labels give you important information so you know how to take the medicine safely and can answer these questions.

- What is the name of the medicine?
- How much do you take and when?
- What are the possible side effects?
- When does the medicine expire?

If you have questions about your medicine, ask the pharmacist. It's their job to answer your questions so you know how to take your medicines the right way.

What will I learn?

- Taking too much medicine is dangerous
- Use a measuring spoon to take the right amount
- You need a prescription from a doctor to buy a prescription medicine
- Read the label to know how to take medicine safely
- A pharmacist can answer your questions about prescription and OTC medicine
- Know the active ingredients in all your OTC medicine

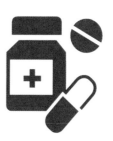

Vocabulary

What new words do you want to learn? Write the words and their definitions here.

Words	Definitions

Prescription (Rx) and
Over-the-Counter Medicine (OTC)

How are they different? How are they the same? Record the answers from your brainstorm in the diagram below.

Prescription   **Over-the-Counter**

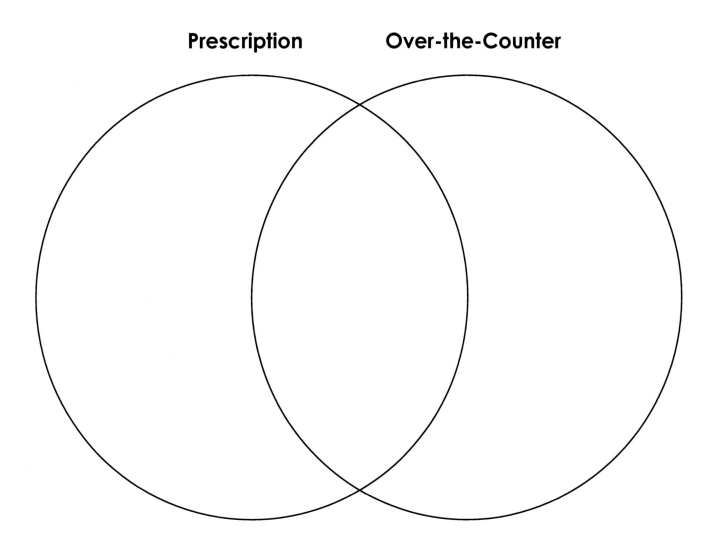

Questions to Ask Your Doctor or Pharmacist

Questions to ask your doctor or pharmacist about your medicine.

- What is the name of this medicine?
- When should I take this medicine?
- How much medicine do I take?
- What are the possible side effects?
- Should I take this medicine with food?
- Can I drink alcohol with this medicine?
- I also take (name of other medicine). Is it OK to take both?

For women:
Always tell your doctor if you are pregnant, nursing, or trying to have a baby!

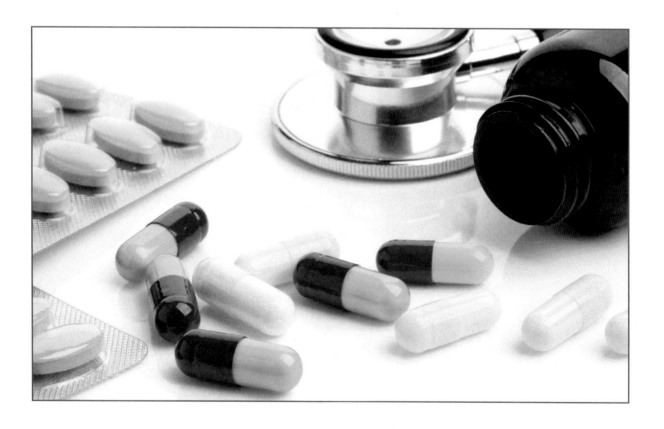

Prescription Abbreviations

What are the abbreviations for each of these words? Write the abbreviations from the box below that matches each word.

1x/day		OTC		2x/day	
Dr.		Rx.	tbsp		tsp

Word(s)	Abbreviation
one time a day	
two times a day	
prescription	
doctor	
over-the-counter	
tablespoon	
teaspoon	

Understanding Warning Labels

Warning labels can give us important information about our medicines. They can tell us about side effects and also about interactions with food, alcohol, and other medicines!

The medicines below belong to Tom. Answer the questions about the warning labels on Tom's medicine.

Which medicine(s) can Tom take with his breakfast? _____

Which medicine(s) might affect Tom's ability to drive a car? _____

Which medicine(s) can Tom take on an empty stomach? _____

Prescription Medicine Label

Read the medicine label to answer these questions.

Hometown Pharmacy
1234 Second Street
Anytown, NY 01234   PHONE   (800) 555-1111

Rx#: **567890-0123**   DR. E MALONE
DATE 3/14/16

MICHAEL J. GARCIA
567 Main Street, Anytown, NY 01234

**TAKE ONE CAPSULE BY MOUTH THREE TIMES DAILY FOR
10 DAYS UNTIL ALL ARE TAKEN**

AMOXICILLIN 500MG CAPSULES   USE BEFORE 3/14/19

NO REFILLS

What is the name of the medicine? _____

What is doctor's name who prescribed the medicine? _____

How much do you take and when? _____

Can you get a refill? How many times? _____

What is the Rx Number? _____

What is the pharmacy's phone number? _____

When does the medicine expire? _____

Over-the-Counter Medicine Label

Read the medicine label to answer these questions.

Drug Facts

Active ingredient (in each caplet)	Purpose
Acetaminophen 500 mg........	Pain reliever/fever reducer

Uses
- temporarily relieves minor aches and pains due to:
  - headache
  - the common cold
  - backache
  - minor pain of arthritis
  - toothache
  - muscular aches
  - premenstrual and menstrual cramps
- temporarily reduces fever

Warnings

Liver warning: This product contains acetaminophen. The maximum daily dose of this product is 6 caplets (3,000 mg) in 24 hours. Severe liver damage may occur if you take
- more than 4,000 mg of acetaminophen in 24 hours
- with other drugs containing acetaminophen
- 3 or more alcoholic drinks every day while using this product

Do not use ■ with any other drug containing acetaminophen (prescription or nonprescription). If you are not sure whether a drug contains acetaminophen, ask a doctor or pharmacist.
- if you have ever had an allergic reaction to this product or any of its ingredients

Ask a doctor before use if you have liver disease

Ask a doctor or pharmacist before use if you are taking the blood thinning drug warfarin

Stop use and ask a doctor if
- pain gets worse or lasts more than 10 days
- fever gets worse or lasts more than 3 days
- new symptoms occur
- redness or swelling is present
These could be signs of a serious condition. ▶

Drug Facts (continued)

If pregnant or breast-feeding, ask a health professional before use.
Keep out of reach of children. In case of overdose, get medical help or contact a Poison Control Center right away. (1-800-222-1222) Quick medical attention is critical for adults as well as for children even if you do not notice any signs or symptoms.

Directions
- do not take more than directed (see Liver warning)

adults and children 12 years and over	■ take 2 caplets every 6 hours while symptoms last ■ do not take more than 6 caplets in 24 hours, unless directed by a doctor ■ do not use for more than 10 days unless directed by a doctor
children under 12 years	ask a doctor

Other information
- store at 20-25°C (68-77°F)

Inactive ingredients carnauba wax*, corn starch*, hypromellose, polyethylene glycol, povidone, pregelatinized starch, sodium starch glycolate*, stearic acid *may contain one or more of these ingredients

Questions? Call 1-800-910-6874

What is the name of the medicine? _____

What is the active ingredient? _____

What is the medicine for? _____

How much medicine should an adult take? _____

What is one warning related to taking this medicine? _____

On My Own: My List of Medicine

Write down what medicines you take. This will be a list of your medicines to share with your doctor. Work on this at home with your family.

Over-the-Counter (OTC) Medicines I take:

Medicine Name	Directions	Why I take this

Prescription (Rx) Medicines I take:

Medicine Name	Directions	Why I take this

Lesson 3: Emergencies

What do you do in an emergency? If the problem is so serious that someone may die without medical attention right away, call 911 or go to an Emergency Room. If the problem is serious but not life-threatening there are also Urgent Care centers where you can get help right away. In most cases, the first thing to do is to call your doctor's office or clinic to talk to a nurse and find out what to do. Sometimes it is a small problem and first aid supplies are all you need.

What will I learn?

- If you think a person might die, call 911 or go to an Emergency Room (ER) at a hospital.
- If it's less serious, call your doctor's office to find out what to do or to make an appointment.
- Call an Urgent Care center if your doctor's office is closed or you cannot get an appointment.

Vocabulary

What new words do you want to learn? Write the words and their definitions here.

Words	Definitions

Should You Call 911?

For each situation, circle YES if you should call 911 or NO if you should not.

1. There is a fire in your home.   YES   NO

2. You locked your keys in your car.   YES   NO

3. You're trying to sleep and your neighbor's dog won't stop barking.   YES   NO

4. Your wife thinks she is having a heart attack   YES   NO

5. Your son fell, hit his head, and is not waking up.   YES   NO

6. You left your wallet on the bus.   YES   NO

7. You were in a car accident, and the other driver is injured.   YES   NO

8. It has snowed, and you can't get your car out of the driveway.   YES   NO

9. Your carbon monoxide detector keeps beeping.   YES   NO

10. You hear someone trying to break into your home.   YES   NO

Calling 911

When to call?
- In emergencies only
  For example: when you need to save a life, stop a crime or report a fire
- If you are not sure, call and let the dispatcher (call taker) decide

Where are you?
- Know the full address of where you are
- Name landmarks, cross streets and mileposts

How to contact?
- Call 911

What next?
- Stay calm and give information
- Listen carefully and follow instructions
- Don't hang up until told to do so
- Call back if you are cut off

If possible...
- Clear walkways
- Put dogs/animals away
- Have someone stand outside to flag down the ambulance

Dialogue Practice: Emergency Calls

Life-threatening Emergencies
- Your neighbor is complaining of bad chest pain
- You see a car crash and the driver is injured
- You have cut your leg and it won't stop bleeding
- You see smoke and flames coming from the house across the street
- Your friend is allergic to peanuts and starts to gasp for air

Use the emergencies listed above to complete the dialogue below. Then practice the dialogue aloud with a partner. Be sure to switch roles with all the emergencies.

Operator: 911. What is your emergency?

Caller: _____. (Fill in emergency)

Operator: What is the location of the emergency?

Caller: I am at _____ St. in _____. (Fill in your address)

Operator: What is your phone number?

Caller: This is my cell phone number _____

Operator: Tell me a little more about this emergency. Is anyone else hurt?

Caller: _____.

Operator: Stay calm and don't hang up. Help is on the way.

Caller: OK, I'll stay on the line.

What to Do In an Emergency

The chart below can help you decide who to call for the care you need.

Routine Care	
Make an appointment with your doctor.	• Regular physical • Treatment for diabetes • Immunizations
Non Life-threatening Emergencies	
First call your doctor's office	• You have the flu • You have a sprained ankle • You have a rash • You are coughing or vomiting
If that doesn't work, call an Urgent Care center	• Your doctor's office is closed • Your doctor or nurse tells you to call an Urgent Care
As a last resort, or if told to go by your doctor or Urgent Care, go to the Emergency Room (ER)	• You can't reach your doctor or an Urgent Care center • Your doctor, nurse or an Urgent Care center tells you to go to the ER
Life-threatening Emergencies	
Call 911	• Breathing trouble • Being unconscious • Bad chest pain • Severe bleeding that won't stop when pressure is applied

On My Own: My Family Emergency Plan

What kinds of emergencies may happen in your family? Talk with your family and write down what you would do.

Non Life-threatening Emergencies

Who do you call to ask what to do?

First, call the Doctor's Office:

Phone#: _____ Notes: _____

What to say: I am a patient. I have a problem. May I talk to a nurse about what I should do?

If that doesn't work, call an Urgent Care center:

Phone#: _____ Notes: _____

What to say: My doctor's office is closed and I have a problem. May I talk to someone for help?

Go to the Emergency Room if told to go by your doctor or Urgent Care, or as a last resort:

Name of Hospital with ER: _____

What to say: My Dr. (or Urgent Care) said that I should come in.

Phone#: _____ Notes: _____

Lesson 4: Appointments

This lesson is about making doctor's appointments. People make appointments to see their doctor when they are sick or have an injury. They also make appointments to see their doctor for checkups, to help them stay healthy.

When you go to the doctor, be sure you have:
- Your medicines
- Your health insurance card
- Your health history information

When you go for a checkup your doctor will recommend screening tests that can help find diseases early when they are easier to treat. If you know you have a disease and follow a treatment plan, you can live better for a long time.

What will I learn?

- Make appointments with the doctor not only when you are sick, but also for checkups to help stay healthy.
- Know your family health history.
- Some diseases have no symptoms. Screening tests can help find diseases early when they are easier to treat.

Vocabulary

What new words do you want to learn? Write the words and their definitions here.

Words	Definitions

Preparing for a Doctor's Appointment

Write down ideas for how you can be prepared before calling to make a doctor's appointment and what to take with you to your doctor's appointment.

Before you call to MAKE an appointment be sure you have:	Before you GO to an appointment be sure you have:

Making a Doctor's Appointment

Fill in the spaces to create a dialogue for making an appointment over the phone. Then practice with a classmate.

Doctor's Office: Hello, Doctor Smith's office.

Patient: Hello, I need an appointment.

Doctor's Office: What is your name and phone number?

Patient: My name is _____. My phone number is _____.

Doctor's Office: And what kind of insurance do you have, _____?

Patient: I have _____ Insurance.

Doctor's Office: What is the reason for your appointment?

Patient: An annual checkup.

Doctor's Office: Can you come at _____ on _____?

Patient: No, that does not work for me. Can the doctor see me another time?

Doctor's Office: Yes, can you come at _____ on _____?

Patient: Thank you. I can come at _____ on _____.

Doctor's Office: Okay, please come fifteen minutes early to fill out your health history form.

Patient: Okay. I can be there fifteen minutes early to fill out forms. Thank you.

Doctor's Office: Thank you. Good-bye.

Patient: Goodbye.

Screening Tests

When you go for a checkup, your doctor will recommend screening tests. Screening tests can help find diseases early when they are easier to treat. Ask your doctor if and when you should be screened for the following diseases.

Diabetes

What is it? High blood sugar

Why get screened? Too much sugar in your blood can damage your:
- Eyes
- Kidneys
- Nerves
- Heart

What is the screening test? A **blood test** can show if you have diabetes.

High Cholesterol

What is it? Cholesterol is made by the body and in fatty foods we eat.

Why get screened? Cholesterol can build-up in the arteries and block the flow of blood to the heart. This can cause:
- Angina (chest pain)
- Heart attack
- Stroke

What is the screening test? A **blood test** can detect high cholesterol.

High Blood Pressure

What is it? Blood pressure is the force blood puts on the artery walls as the heart pump.

Why get screened? High blood pressure can cause health problems like:
- Stroke
- Heart attack
- Kidney failure

What is the screening test? A **blood pressure cuff** is placed around your upper arm and can measure blood pressure.

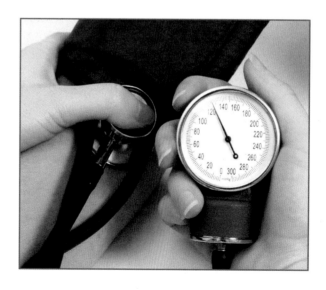

Doctor measuring blood pressure

Screening Tests

Breast Cancer

What is it? Cancer in the breast.

Why get screened?
- One in 8 women gets breast cancer
- Breast cancer often has not symptoms
- The chance of getting breast cancer goes up as a woman gets older

What is the screening test? A **mammogram** can detect breast cancer early when it is easier to treat.

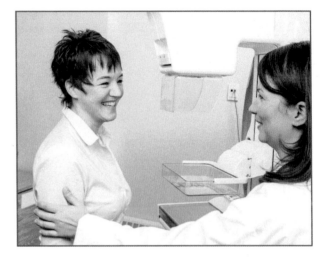

Woman getting a mammogram

Colon Cancer

What is it? Cancer in the colon. The colon is part of the large intestine.

Why get screened?
- Colon cancer is common in both men and women
- The chance of getting colon cancer goes up after age 50

What is the screening test? A **colonoscopy** allows your doctor to check the entire colon for early signs of cancer.

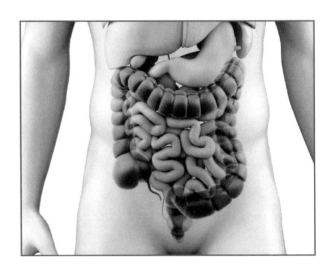

Colon in the body

On My Own: My Health History Form

Fill in this health history form. Then you'll have the information to take with you to your next doctor's appointment.

Health History Form:

Name: _____ Date of Birth (DOB): _____

Address: _____ Telephone: _____

_____

Gender (circle one): Female   Male

Please select one: ☐ Single ☐ Married ☐ Divorced ☐ Widowed

What is the reason for your appointment today?

_____

_____

Current Medications
What medications do you take?
(Prescription medication and over-the-counter medication)

_____

_____

Allergies

_____

_____

Illness or Operation
Please list all serious illnesses and operations you have experienced.

Illness or Operation	Year of Illness/Operation	Were you hospitalized? (Write YES or NO)

Family Health History

	Does anyone in your family have it?	Who has it? (mother, father, sister, brother, grandparent)
High Blood Pressure		
Heart Disease		
Diabetes		
Cancer		

Emergency Contact Name: _____

Emergency Contact Phone Number: _____

Relationship to you: _____

Lesson 5: Talking to the Doctor

This lesson is about talking with your doctor. When you go to the doctor be sure to describe your symptoms and tell your doctor what you are worried about. If something hurts or feels bad, your doctor needs to know. Your doctor also needs to know what medicines you are taking. Your doctor can help you better if you describe your symptoms and talk about your health concerns.

You should also ask your doctor questions. Asking your doctor questions will help you and your doctor decide what is best. Write down your questions before you go to your appointment. This will help you remember to ask all your questions.

If you do not understand what your doctor says, ask your doctor to tell you again or explain in a different way. Try asking these questions:
- Can you please say that again?
- Can you show me?
- I don't understand. Can you say it in a different way?

What will I learn?

- Describe your symptoms to the doctor. Bring a friend or ask for an interpreter if you need help.
- Make sure you understand what the doctor says. If you don't understand, ask the doctor to say it again or to show you.
- Ask questions when you are with the doctor. Write them down ahead of time so you don't forget.

Vocabulary

What new words do you want to learn? Write the words and their definitions here.

Words	Definitions

Being Prepared for a Doctor's Visit

Use Pages 20-22 in *Staying Healthy* to fill in this chart.

What can you do to prepare for a doctor's visit?	What happens during a doctor's visit?

Describing Your Symptoms

Use the information on this page to describe your symptoms. Practice with a classmate.

When/Timing

When did it start?
Yesterday, the day before yesterday, last week, a week ago, the week before last, last month, two years ago, etc.

How long does it last?
10 minutes, an hour all morning, three days, until I lie down, etc.

When does it happen?
Every morning, at work when I am stressed, whenever I eat/exert myself/exercise/stand up quickly, etc.

How Much/Severity

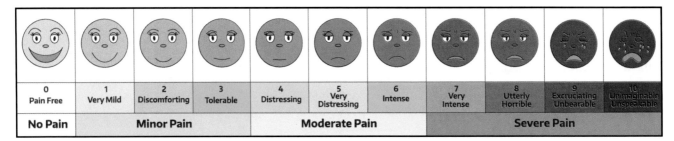

0 Pain Free	1 Very Mild	2 Discomforting	3 Tolerable	4 Distressing	5 Very Distressing	6 Intense	7 Very Intense	8 Utterly Horrible	9 Excruciating Unbearable	10 Unimaginable Unspeakable
No Pain	**Minor Pain**			**Moderate Pain**			**Severe Pain**			

How Often/Frequency

Always, Regularly	90 to 100% of the time (every day or several days a week
Usually, Often, Frequently	70 to 80% of the time (one or two days a week)
Sometimes, Occasionally	50% of the time (twice a month)
Rarely, Hardly Ever	20-40% of the time (three times a year)
Never	0 to 10% of the time (once a year, if at all)

Answering Questions

Read Case Study #1 below. Have your partner be the doctor and ask you the questions from the page. You be the patient and answer the questions based on the case study. Then switch roles and do the same using Case Study #2.

Case Study #1:

For the past three days, you have had a sharp pain in your stomach. On the pain scale where 0 is no pain and 10 is the worst pain, this pain is about an 8 on the scale. It's there most of the day and is worse when you walk. The only time it feels a little better is when you lie down.

Case Study #2:

Your lower back has been bothering you for a few months. You lift heavy boxes for your job and it is very painful at the end of the day. There is a dull ache for about half of the day, and in the evening if you bend down to tie your shoe, there is sharp pain that is so severe you can barely stand up again.

Question Your Doctor Asks:

- How long have you had the pain?
- How painful is it?
- How often does this happen?
- Where is your pain?
- Does the pain spread to other parts of the body?
- How much does it hurt?
- What does it feel like?
- Is it worse at any time of the day?
- What makes the pain feel better?

Talking to the Doctor

Questions you ask your doctor:	Possible responses:
What is my diagnosis?	You have the flu You have an infection You have high blood pressure You have diabetes
What are my treatment options?	You can take medicine We can remove that You may need surgery If you lose 20 pounds, you may not need to take medicine
Why do I need to take this medicine?	This medicine will... • ease the pain • reduce swelling • lower your blood pressure • control your blood sugar

Other questions:

_____

_____

_____

What to Do If You Don't Understand

What questions will you ask your doctor if you don't understand?

Example: Can you repeat that, please?

_____

_____

_____

_____

One way to check your understanding is to repeat back to the doctor what you think the doctor said. How do you do this? What will you say?

Example: Can I repeat that to make sure I understand?

_____

_____

_____

_____

On My Own: My Symptoms and Questions

What do you want to tell your doctor or ask about? Write down your symptoms, worries and questions here.

Symptoms and Questions:

My Symptoms:

_____

_____

_____

_____

My Questions:

_____

_____

_____

_____

For more information about asking questions, go to: ahrq.gov/questions

Lesson 6: It's My Health

There is a lot you can do for yourself and your family to stay healthy. This includes being active, managing stress, keeping teeth healthy, and avoiding unhealthy habits, like smoking, drinking alcohol and using drugs. One of the best ways to stay healthy is to NOT smoke.

Taking care of your health also means getting the health care you need. You have a right and responsibility to get the health care you need when you visit the doctor.

You have a right to:
- Ask questions
- Have an interpreter
- Understand your health care

You have a responsibility to
- Tell your doctor what you are feeling
- Make sure you understand your health care

What will I learn?

These are things you can do to stay healthy:
- Be active every day and maintain a healthy weight
- Manage your stress
- Brush and floss your teeth
- Don't smoke or use other drugs
- Get the health care you need
- Find reliable health information online

Vocabulary

What new words do you want to learn? Write the words and their definitions here.

Words	Definitions

Taking Care of My Teeth

The hard, outer layer of your teeth is called enamel. Tooth decay is the destruction of this enamel. It can be a problem for children, teens and adults. This is how it happens: plaque, a sticky film of bacteria, constantly forms on your teeth. The bacteria in plaque produce acids that attack tooth enamel. The stickiness of the plaque keeps these acids in contact with your teeth and over time the enamel can break down. This is when cavities can form.

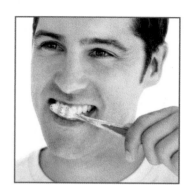

Select the best word from the word bank to fit each sentence.

	six		fluoride		two
before		cavities		plaque	enamel

1. Always brush your teeth _____ bedtime and after every meal if at all possible.

2. Flossing helps remove _____ from between the teeth.

3. Vitamins and calcium help strengthen _____.

4. You should get a dental cleaning and check-up every _____ months.

5. Use toothpaste that contains _____.

6. Brush for no less than _____ minutes.

7. Good dental care can prevent _____.

Body Mass Index (BMI) Chart

Use the chart to calculate your BMI. Find your weight on vertical axis. Find you height on the horizontal axis. Locate your BMI on the chart. What else does the chart tell you about your BMI?

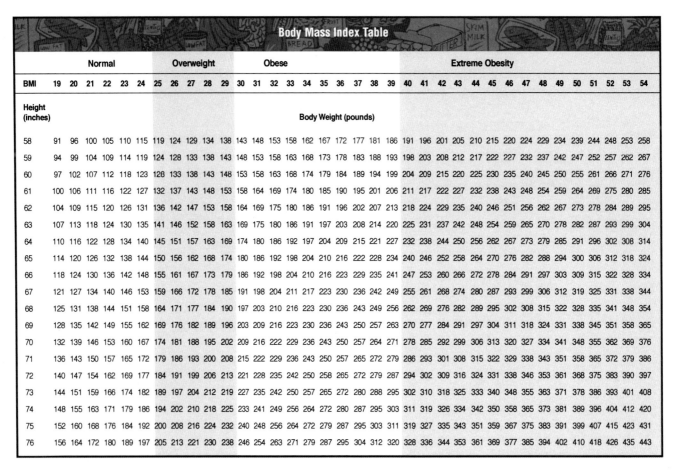

Body Mass Index Table

	Normal						Overweight					Obese									Extreme Obesity														
BMI	19	20	21	22	23	24	25	26	27	28	29	30	31	32	33	34	35	36	37	38	39	40	41	42	43	44	45	46	47	48	49	50	51	52	53	54
Height (inches)																	**Body Weight (pounds)**																			
58	91	96	100	105	110	115	119	124	129	134	138	143	148	153	158	162	167	172	177	181	186	191	196	201	205	210	215	220	224	229	234	239	244	248	253	258
59	94	99	104	109	114	119	124	128	133	138	143	148	153	158	163	168	173	178	183	188	193	198	203	208	212	217	222	227	232	237	242	247	252	257	262	267
60	97	102	107	112	118	123	128	133	138	143	148	153	158	163	168	174	179	184	189	194	199	204	209	215	220	225	230	235	240	245	250	255	261	266	271	276
61	100	106	111	116	122	127	132	137	143	148	153	158	164	169	174	180	185	190	195	201	206	211	217	222	227	232	238	243	248	254	259	264	269	275	280	285
62	104	109	115	120	126	131	136	142	147	153	158	164	169	175	180	186	191	196	202	207	213	218	224	229	235	240	246	251	256	262	267	273	278	284	289	295
63	107	113	118	124	130	135	141	146	152	158	163	169	175	180	186	191	197	203	208	214	220	225	231	237	242	248	254	259	265	270	278	282	287	293	299	304
64	110	116	122	128	134	140	145	151	157	163	169	174	180	186	192	197	204	209	215	221	227	232	238	244	250	256	262	267	273	279	285	291	296	302	308	314
65	114	120	126	132	138	144	150	156	162	168	174	180	186	192	198	204	210	216	222	228	234	240	246	252	258	264	270	276	282	288	294	300	306	312	318	324
66	118	124	130	136	142	148	155	161	167	173	179	186	192	198	204	210	216	223	229	235	241	247	253	260	266	272	278	284	291	297	303	309	315	322	328	334
67	121	127	134	140	146	153	159	166	172	178	185	191	198	204	211	217	223	230	236	242	249	255	261	268	274	280	287	293	299	306	312	319	325	331	338	344
68	125	131	138	144	151	158	164	171	177	184	190	197	203	210	216	223	230	236	243	249	256	262	269	276	282	289	295	302	308	315	322	328	335	341	348	354
69	128	135	142	149	155	162	169	176	182	189	196	203	209	216	223	230	236	243	250	257	263	270	277	284	291	297	304	311	318	324	331	338	345	351	358	365
70	132	139	146	153	160	167	174	181	188	195	202	209	216	222	229	236	243	250	257	264	271	278	285	292	299	306	313	320	327	334	341	348	355	362	369	376
71	136	143	150	157	165	172	179	186	193	200	208	215	222	229	236	243	250	257	265	272	279	286	293	301	308	315	322	329	338	343	351	358	365	372	379	386
72	140	147	154	162	169	177	184	191	199	206	213	221	228	235	242	250	258	265	272	279	287	294	302	309	316	324	331	338	346	353	361	368	375	383	390	397
73	144	151	159	166	174	182	189	197	204	212	219	227	235	242	250	257	265	272	280	288	295	302	310	318	325	333	340	348	355	363	371	378	386	393	401	408
74	148	155	163	171	179	186	194	202	210	218	225	233	241	249	256	264	272	280	287	295	303	311	319	326	334	342	350	358	365	373	381	389	396	404	412	420
75	152	160	168	176	184	192	200	208	216	224	232	240	248	256	264	272	279	287	295	303	311	319	327	335	343	351	359	367	375	383	391	399	407	415	423	431
76	156	164	172	180	189	197	205	213	221	230	238	246	254	263	271	279	287	295	304	312	320	328	336	344	353	361	369	377	385	394	402	410	418	426	435	443

Source: National Heart, Lung, and Blood Institute; National Institutes of Health; U.S. Department of Health and Human Services.

Impacts of Smoking, Alcohol and Drugs on the Body

What are the impacts of smoking, alcohol and drug use on the body? Discuss with others. Write your findings in the columns.

Smoking	Alcohol	Drugs

Taking Care of Stress

....on your body
- Headache
- Muscle tension or pain
- Chest pain
- Fatigue
- Change in sex drive
- Stomach upset
- Sleep problems

...on your mood
- Anxiety
- Depression
- Lack of motivation
- Lack of focus
- Anger
- Sadness
- Depression

What are some healthy ways to manage stress?

_____

_____

_____

Sometimes stress is so bad that it can affect work and family life in a serious way. What can you do if the stress is very bad?

_____

_____

_____

My Rights and Responsibilities

Patient rights:

What the doctors, nurses and hospitals must do for the patient

- Disclose all relevant information to the patient
- Provide patients with access to emergency services
- Be respectful and not discriminate
- Keep patient information confidential

Patient Responsibilities:

Ways in which a patient can work with a health care provider to achieve the best quality health outcome:

- Be involved in health care decisions
- Provide complete and true information
- Notify your doctor if you do not understand
- Report any dissatisfaction with your care

My Health Journal

This journal can be a place for you to record information about your health.

Date	Problem or Symptom (Note when it started)	Medicine (Note Prescription or OTC and if the medicine helped)	Doctor's Visit, Hospitalization or Surgery (Note the date, time and doctor's name)

On My Own: Finding Health Information Online

How can you tell if you can trust the information? Ask these questions:

- Is it up-to-date? When was the website published or last updated?
- Who put this information online? Look to see if it's a source you can trust
- What is the purpose of the website? Is it to sell you something?

To learn more, look at **Evaluating Health Information** and try their online tutorial: nlm.nih.gov/medlineplus/evaluatinghealthinformation.html

The best way to find health information online is to go to a website you know you can trust! Try these recommended websites:

- **MedlinePlus:** medlineplus.gov
- **KidsHealth:** kidshealth.org
- **Healthfinder:** healthfinder.gov

Lesson 7: Review
What did I learn?

Lesson 1: Healthy Eating

- Eat healthy to be healthy.
- Eat more fruits and vegetables.
- A healthy plate includes foods from all food groups.
- Use nutrition facts labels to make healthy food choices.
- Eating too much and being overweight can cause health problems.
- Make healthy ingredient substitutions when preparing food at home.

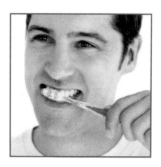

Lesson 2: Medicine

- Taking too much medicine is dangerous.
- Use a measuring spoon to take the right amount.
- You need a prescription from a doctor to buy a prescription medicine.
- Read the label to know how to take medicine safely.

Lesson 3: Emergency

- If you think a person might die, call 911 or go to an Emergency Room (ER) at a hospital.
- If it's less serious, call your doctor's office to find out what to do, or to make an appointment.
- Call an Urgent Care Center if your doctor's office is closed or you can't get an appointment.
- Prepare a first aid kit for your home, and learn how to use the items in it.

Lesson 4: Appointments

- Make appointments with the doctor not only when you are sick, but also for checkups to help stay healthy.
- Communicate with your doctor to plan for appropriate medical screenings.

Lesson 5: Talking to the Doctor

- Describe your symptoms to the doctor. Bring a friend or ask for an interpreter if you need help.
- Make sure you understand what the doctor says. If you don't understand, ask the doctor to say it again or to show you.
- Ask questions when you are with the doctor. Write them down ahead of time so you don't forget.

Lesson 6: My Health

These are things you can do to stay healthy:

- Be active every day
- Manage your weight
- Manage your stress
- Brush and floss your teeth
- Don't smoke
- Get the health care you need

How can I keep using this workbook?

- Review the information after the class is finished.
- Talk about it with your friends and family.
- Look at your On My Own pages.
- Review the vocabulary.
- Take it with you to your appointments.
- Practice the questions to ask your doctor.
- Remember to do the things you wrote about.

**Good Luck!
Good Health!**

Made in the USA
Columbia, SC
12 June 2019